Pillbots

Description

After observing the structures and behaviors of pill bugs, students design a solution to a human problem through biomimicry, the design of technologies that are modeled on the structures of living things. They learn about some pill bug–inspired technologies, as well as some other examples of biomimicry, and then design a device that mimics a pill bug's structures and behaviors in order to solve a problem.

Alignment With the *Next Generation Science Standards*

Performance Expectations

1-LS1-1: Use materials to design a solution to a human problem by mimicking how plants and/or animals use their external parts to help them survive, grow, and meet their needs.

K-2-ETS1-2: Develop a simple sketch, drawing, or physical model to illustrate how the shape of an object helps it function as needed to solve a given problem.

Science and Engineering Practice	Disciplinary Core Ideas	Crosscutting Concepts
Developing and Using Models Develop a simple model based on evidence to represent a proposed object or tool.	LS1.A: Structure and Function All organisms have external parts. Different animals use their body parts in different ways to see, hear, grasp objects, protect themselves, move from place to place, and seek, find, and take in food, water, and air. ETS1.B: Developing Possible Solutions Designs can be conveyed through sketches, drawings, or physical models. These representations are useful in communicating ideas for a problem's solutions to other people.	Structure and Function The shape and stability of structures of natural and designed objects are related to their function. Influence of Engineering, Technology, and Science on Society and the Natural World People depend on various technologies in their lives; human life would be very different without technology.

Note: The activities in this lesson will help students move toward the performance expectations listed, which is the goal after multiple activities. However, the activities will not by themselves be sufficient to reach the performance expectations.

Featured Picture Books

TITLE: ***Next Time You See a Pill Bug***
AUTHOR: **Emily Morgan**
PUBLISHER: **NSTA Kids**
YEAR: **2013**
GENRE: **Non-Narrative Information**
SUMMARY: *This book invites children and adults to interact with these fascinating animals and learn about their extraordinary features.*

TITLE: ***National Geographic Kids: Robots***
AUTHOR: **Melissa Stewart**
PUBLISHER: **National Geographic Children's Books**
YEAR: **2014**
GENRE: **Non-Narrative Information**
SUMMARY: *Young readers will learn about the most fascinating robots of today and tomorrow in this colorful, photo-packed book.*

Time Needed

This lesson will take several class periods. Suggested scheduling is as follows:

Session 1: Engage with Next Time You See a Pill Bug Introduction, Explore with Pill Bug Observations, and Explain with Next Time You See a Pill Bug Read-Aloud

Session 2: Explain with Biomimicry: Pillbot Video and National Geographic Kids: Robots Read-Aloud

Session 3: Elaborate with Pillbot Designs and Evaluate with My Pillbot

Materials

For Pill Bug Observations (per student)

- Pill bugs
- Clear plastic container (with sides high enough to contain the pill bugs, or use a lid with tiny air holes punched through it)
- Piece of paper towel small enough to cover ½ of container bottom, dampened with water from a clean spray bottle
- Hand lens

SAFETY

- Ensure that pill bugs do not become dehydrated, are not too hot or cold, and are not handled roughly.
- Remind students that all living things should be handled gently.
- Wash hands with soap and water after completing this activity.

Student Pages

- Pill Bug Observations
- My Pillbot
- STEM Everywhere

Background for Teachers

Turn over a rock or rotting log nearly anywhere in the United States, and (if the weather is mild) you are likely to find a pill bug! Pill bugs, also called roly-polies, are small terrestrial isopods abundant in temperate areas throughout the world. Because they are engaging, harmless, and easily collected, they provide an excellent opportunity for children to learn about invertebrate body parts and behaviors. In this lesson, students also learn how studying common pill bugs has led roboticists to some exciting technologies that mimic their structures and functions.

A pill bug

Although many students might think of pill bugs as bugs or insects, they are neither. Pill bugs are actually crustaceans, like lobsters, shrimp, and crabs. But pill bugs are unusual crustaceans because they live their entire lives on land. Like all crustaceans, pill bugs breathe through gills. Their gills must be moist for them to breathe. However, pill bugs are not able to breathe underwater like their crustacean relatives, so it is important to store them in a place that is damp but not too wet. A small aquarium or plastic container with moist soil is all you need to store them safely in the classroom. Pill bugs have 14 legs, 2 antennae, and 2 eyes, and their exoskeletons are divided into many segments. The most notable behavior of the pill bug is its ability to roll into a ball when it feels threatened.

Researchers in South Korea and Germany have developed technologies that mimic the structures and behaviors of pill bugs to solve human problems. German researchers have created a prototype for the OLE (pronounced "oh-luh") pill bug to detect and fight forest fires. They have scaled up the pill bug's form to the size of a St. Bernard. But instead of having 14 legs like a pill bug, OLE only has 6. These enormous, 200 lb. robots scuttle around the forest floor at speeds of 6–12 miles per hour and use infrared "biosensors" to detect fire sources. To protect itself, the OLE has a segmented shell that allows it to curl into a ball just like a real pill bug. This ceramic-fiber compound shell can withstand temperatures of more than 2300°F! According to researchers, 30 OLEs could protect a forest as large as 2,700 square miles.

Roboticists in South Korea have designed a robot called the pillbot that mimics a pill bug. This robot is about the size of a softball, and it has two modes: protection and locomotion. In protection mode, the pillbot rolls into a ball and can be "bowled" into a location that is too dangerous for humans. Once it reaches the target, it unrolls into locomotion mode and can then move around and collect information in this dangerous area. See the "Websites" section at the end of this lesson for more information about these pill bug–inspired robots.

OLE and the pillbot are examples of biomimicry, the practice of designing nature-inspired solutions to human problems. This field of science is known as biomimetics. One of the most well-known examples of biomimicry is the invention of Velcro (see Biomimicry Photo Gallery in the "Websites" section). Swiss inventor George de Mestral noticed how strongly cockleburs stuck to his pants after a walk through the woods, so he decided to look closely at them under a microscope. He observed that the burs were covered in small hooks and that the hooks caught the loops in the fabric of his pants. This observation inspired him to design a loop-and-hook fastening system, which we now know as Velcro. Olympians wear swimsuits that mimic sharkskin, underwater communication devices mimic the sounds that dolphins send through the water, NASA has suggested the development of aircraft that are modeled on the shape of twirling maple seeds, and the list goes on and on.

In this lesson, students begin by observing the structures and behaviors of a familiar animal, the pill bug. They read about some pill bug–inspired technologies as well as some other examples of biomimicry. Then they are challenged to design a pillbot to solve a human problem. Students explore the science and engineering practice (SEP) of developing and using models as they use sketches and drawings to represent their proposed solution. Students are also engaged in the crosscutting concept (CCC) of structure and function throughout the lesson.

Learning Progressions

Below are the disciplinary core idea (DCI) grade band endpoints for grades K–2 and 3–5. These are provided to show how student understanding of the DCIs in this lesson will progress in future grade levels.

DCIs	Grades K–2	Grades 3–5
LS1.A: Structure and Function	• All organisms have external parts. Different animals use their body parts in different ways to see, hear, grasp objects, protect themselves, move from place to place, and seek, find, and take in food, water, and air.	• Plants and animals have both internal and external structures that serve various functions in growth, survival, behavior, and reproduction.
ETS1.B: Developing Possible Solutions	• Designs can be conveyed through sketches, drawings, or physical models. These representations are useful in communicating ideas for a problem's solutions to other people.	• At whatever stage, communicating with peers about proposed solutions is an important part of the design process, and shared ideas can lead to improved designs.

Source: Willard, T., ed. (2015). The NSTA quick-reference guide to the NGSS: Elementary school. Arlington, VA: NSTA Press.

engage

Next Time You See a Pill Bug Introduction

Making Connections: Text to Self

Show students the cover of Next Time You See a Pill Bug and introduce the author, Emily Morgan. Tell them that as a child, the author enjoyed exploring the outdoors, looking under rocks and logs to see what was living there. Now, she and her son like to explore the woods in their backyard together, collecting pill bugs and other living things to observe. Ask

? Have you ever collected pill bugs or played with them?

? Where did you find them?

? What did you do with them?

? What did you notice about the way they look? The way they move?

Read aloud only pages 6–7, which encourage students to pick up a pill bug and let it crawl around on their hands, observe it closely, and describe it. Tell students that they are going to have an opportunity to do just that!

explore

Pill Bug Observations

In advance, collect some live pill bugs from the local environment (at least one per student), and keep them in a temporary habitat containing some damp paper towels or damp leaf litter. Make sure the sides of the container are high enough that the pill bugs cannot escape (or use a lid with tiny air holes punched through). You can also have your students collect the pill bugs for homework and bring them to class for this activity.

Give each student a Pill Bug Observations student page and a hand lens. Tell them that

OBSERVING A PILL BUG

they will be closely observing pill bugs to learn more about their body parts and behaviors. Remind them to treat the pill bugs gently, then give each student a pill bug in a clear plastic container with half of the bottom covered with a piece of damp paper towel. (Students will be observing whether the pill bugs seem to prefer damp or dry places, so it is important not to cover the entire container bottom with the damp paper towel.) Review how to use a magnifier properly: Put your eye close to the lens, shut the other eye, and move the container close until the pill bug comes into focus. Students will observe the pill bug, make a detailed sketch, and label the parts they know. They try to count the legs (all 14 of them!), make observations of its body parts, and observe and record the pill bug's reactions to different stimuli in a chart.

explain

Next Time You See a Pill Bug Read-Aloud

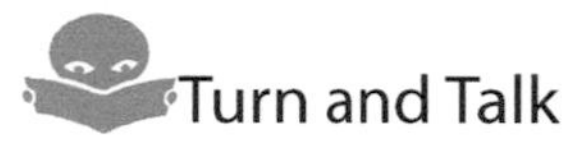

Turn and Talk

Have students explain what they have observed by sharing their drawings and observations with a partner. Then, ask

- ? What body parts did you notice on the pill bugs? (Students may notice legs, eyes, antennae, and segments. Allow them to call these features by other names and/or use gestures to communicate the features they identify.)
- ? How many legs were you able to count? (Answers will vary because pill bug legs are small and wiggly, but they have 14.)
- ? What did you notice about your pill bug's behavior in response to your actions? (Students may notice the pill bug moving away from their touch, flipping itself back over, rolling into a ball, or moving toward the damp paper towel.)
- ? What body parts helped the pill bug do those things? (Legs help them move and flip over, overlapping segments help them roll into a ball, antennae help them find the damp paper towel, etc.)

> **CCC: Structure and Function**
> The shape and stability of structures of natural objects are related to their function(s).

Emphasize the crosscutting concept of structure and function by asking the following:

- ? How might the pill bug's body parts and behaviors help it survive and grow? (Answers will vary, but students may suggest that legs help the pill bug move to find water, food, or escape predators; the hard segments may help it roll up to protect its soft underside from predators; and the antennae may help it find its way in dark places in order to stay safe.)
- ? What are you wondering about pill bugs? (Answers will vary.)

> Connecting to the Common Core
> **Reading: Informational Text**
> Key Ideas and Details: 1.1

Determining Importance

Now, tell students that you are going to share the rest of the book Next Time You See a Pill Bug and that this book will help them understand some of the pill bug structures and behaviors they observed earlier.

After reading, ask

- ? Many of you noticed that your pill bug moved back to the damp paper towel when you moved it to a dry place. Why do you think it did so? (Pill bugs need to stay in damp or moist areas so they can breathe.)
- ? What parts do pill bugs use to breathe? (gills)

Explain that rather than breathing through mouths like we do, pill bugs have these special structures underneath their bodies where they can take in air. In order for the gills to work, they have to be moist. Ask

- ? Many of you noticed that your pill bug rolled up when you touched it or turned it over. Why do you think it did so? (It felt threatened or scared.)
- ? What body parts help the pill bug roll up? (its segments or its segmented exoskeleton)
- ? How does this help the pill bug survive? (The hard segments on the exoskeleton protect the soft underside of the pill bug. This keeps the pill bug from getting squashed and can protect it if it falls.)

> **CCC: Structure and Function**
> The shape and stability of structures of natural objects are related to their function(s).

Revisit page 15 of the book, which shows a pill bug flattened out and then rolled up into a ball to protect itself. Students should be able to see from the pictures how the exoskeleton protects the inner, softer part of its body. Explain that this defense mechanism is so unique and special that

roboticists, or engineers who design robots, have actually tried to copy it!

Biomimicry: Pillbot Video

Making Connections: Text to World

Tell students that a team of roboticists in South Korea has created a working robot called the pillbot. The pillbot is based on many of the structures and abilities of real pill bugs. Show students the video titled "Pillbot" listed in the "Websites" section.

Then ask

? What structures did you notice on the pillbot that are similar to a pill bug? (hard, overlapping segments and legs)

? What do these structures help the pillbot do? (crawl over obstacles and roll into a ball)

? What human problems do you think a robotic pill bug could solve? (Answers will vary.)

Explain that this little robot is about the size of a softball. The overlapping plates allow it to roll up and be rolled into a location that is too dangerous for humans. Once it reaches the target point, it unrolls and then crawls around on its legs and collects information. Roboticists in Germany are working on another type of pillbot—the OLE (pronounced "oh-luh") pill bug, which could someday be used to fight forest fires. It carries water and fire extinguishers and has a fireproof exoskeleton. The robot's fireproof armor protects the equipment inside of it much like a pill bug's exoskeleton protects the inside of its body. Explain that engineers often look to nature for ideas. Imitating living things to solve a human problem is called biomimicry. The prefix bio means "life" and the word mimic means "to imitate." So the invention of robotic pillbots is an example of biomimicry—"imitating life."

National Geographic Kids: Robots Read-Aloud

Connecting to the Common Core
Reading: Informational Text
Key Ideas and Details: 1.1

Chunking

Show students the cover of the book National Geographic Kids: Robots, and ask if they know what a robot is. You will likely get a wide variety of responses. In fact, engineers themselves don't always agree on the definition of robot. Explain that because the book is nonfiction, you can enter the text at any point. You don't have to read the book from cover to cover if you are looking for specific information. Tell students that you will be reading the parts of the book that explain how engineers sometimes look to nature for inspiration. Read and discuss pages 4–7, which describe these characteristics of a robot:

- Has movable parts
- Can make decisions
- Is designed by people to do a job by itself
- Collects information from its surroundings
- Processes the information and figures out what to do next
- Does only things it is programmed to do

Questioning

Then ask

? What makes a pillbot a robot? (It has movable parts, it is designed to do a job by itself, it collects information, etc.)

Tell students to listen carefully as you read another section of the book. This section gives more examples of biomimicry—robots inspired by nature. Have students listen for the different

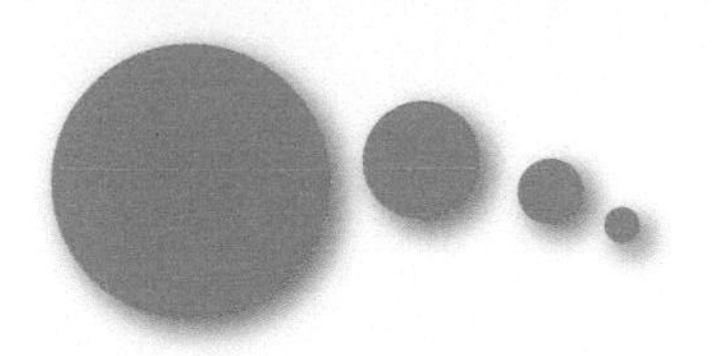

kinds of animals that roboticists study as they design robots. Read aloud pages 16–21 of National Geographic Kids: Robots, making sure to share the photographs and insets as you read. Then share another example of biomimicry by reading about the Robotuna pictured on page 13.

After reading, ask

- ? What is the branch of science called that uses biomimicry (borrowing ideas from nature)? (biomimetics)
- ? What kinds of animals did roboticists study to design the robots you learned about? (ladybugs, geckos, dogs, jellyfish, snakes, fish)
- ? Why do roboticists study animals? (to get ideas for solving design problems)
- ? Can you guess what animal roboticists have studied more than any other animal in the world? (humans!)

Then read pages 32–33 about humanlike robots. Explain that studying how humans move and behave is also an example of biomimicry. For more examples of biomimicry, see the "Websites" section for a photo gallery.

elaborate

Pillbot Designs

Tell students they are going to have the opportunity to design their very own robot! They will be using biomimicry by studying the body parts and movements of pill bugs to invent a pillbot. The purpose of designing a pillbot is to solve a human problem or need. You may want to have students observe live pill bugs again to get inspiration for their pillbot designs. Alternatively, you can view a video segment that gives a close-up view of the pill bug's body parts and behaviors, such as "Pill Bug" (see the "Websites" section for the video link).

> **CCC: Structure and Function**
> The shape and stability of structures of natural and designed objects are related to their function(s).

Begin the brainstorming process by discussing questions such as the following:

- ? What are some unique body parts you noticed when observing your pill bug? (14 legs, antennae, hard exoskeleton, segments, etc.)
- ? What are some unique movements or behaviors you noticed when observing your pill bugs? (They roll up when threatened, they crawl over things, they flip over when turned on their backs, etc.)
- ? What are some human problems that a pillbot's body parts might help solve? (Answers will vary.)
- ? Are there places that are unsafe for humans that a pillbot might be able to explore? (Answers will vary.)
- ? Are there jobs that a robotic pill bug could do that humans could not? (Answers will vary.)
- ? Are there toys or devices that could be inspired by a pill bug's movements or body parts? (Answers will vary.)

Then brainstorm some pillbot ideas together. Examples might include an expandable backpack that automatically rolls up for storage when it is empty, a device that transports something by rolling up into a ball and then unrolling when it reaches its destination, a modified soccer ball that rolls up when it is kicked and then unrolls and moves by itself to make the game more fun and interesting, and so on.

evaluate

My Pillbot

Connecting to the Common Core
Writing
TEXT TYPES AND PURPOSES: 1.3

Writing

SEP: Developing and Using Models
Develop a simple model based on evidence to represent a proposed object or tool.

Have each student select an idea from your brainstorming session or have students come up with ideas on their own. Give each student a copy of the My Pillbot student page, and have them begin designing their pillbots. Students should be able to make a simple, labeled sketch of their pillbot; describe the human problem the pillbot solves; identify the structure on their pillbot that is like a real pill bug; and compare how the pill bug uses that part to how the pillbot uses that part.

Name: Kayla B.
Chapter 13

My Pillbot

Name of my pillbot: packy

Labeled sketch of my pillbot:

1. The problem my pillbot solves: carry my books.

2. The part of my pillbot that is like a real pill bug: The segments

3. A real pill bug uses this part to roll up and protec

4. My pillbot uses this part to unroll to fill and roll up to fit on my back.

Picture-Perfect STEM Lessons, Grade 1, Expanded Edition 193

MY PILLBOT

Bring students back together to share their pillbot designs. As they share, discuss how each pillbot's external parts are based on a real pill bug's external parts. To facilitate this discussion, ask questions such as the following:

? How are the parts of the pillbot similar to the parts of a real pill bug?

? How does the pillbot use those parts to solve the problem?

? How does a real pill bug use those parts to help it survive?

STEM Everywhere

Give students the STEM Everywhere student page as a way to involve their families and extend their learning. They can do the activity with an adult helper and share their results with the class. If students do not have access to the materials or the internet at home, you may choose to have them complete this activity at school.

Continued

Opportunities for Differentiated Instruction

This box lists questions and challenges related to the lesson that students may select to research, investigate, or innovate. Students may also use the questions as examples to help them generate their own questions. These questions can help you move your students from the teacher-directed investigation to engaging in the science and engineering practices in a more student-directed format.

Extra Support

For students who are struggling to meet the lesson objectives, provide a question and guide them in the process of collecting research or helping them design procedures or solutions.

Extensions

For students with high interest or who have already met the lesson objectives, have them choose a question (or pose their own question), conduct their own research, and design their own procedures or solutions.

After selecting one of the questions in this box or formulating their own questions, students can individually or collaboratively make predictions, design investigations or surveys to test their predictions, collect evidence, devise explanations, design solutions, or examine related resources. They can communicate their findings through a science notebook, at a poster session or gallery walk, or by producing a media project.

Research

Have students brainstorm researchable questions:

? Where do pill bugs live?

? What are some other types of isopods, and where do they live?

? What are some other examples of biomimicry?

Investigate

Have students brainstorm testable questions to be solved through science or math:

? Do pill bugs prefer bright places or dark places?

- ? What types of food do pill bugs prefer?
- ? Can a pill bug find its way through a maze?

Innovate

Have students brainstorm problems to be solved through engineering:

- ? How could you use biomimicry to invent something that is based on how an elephant uses its trunk?
- ? How could you use biomimicry to invent something that is based on how a snake moves?
- ? How could you use biomimicry to invent something that is based on how a maple seed spins through the air?

Websites

Biomimicry Photo Gallery
http://inhabitat.com/finding-design-inspiration-in-nature-biomimicry-for-a-better-planet

"The Firefighting Robot" (article)
Note: The pill bug is inaccurately referred to as an insect. www.popsci.com/scitech/article/2008-03/firefighting-robot

"OLE Pill Bug Robot" (article)
www.engadget.com/2007/08/12/ole-pill-bug-robot-concept-could-fight-forest-fires

"Pillbot" (video)
www.youtube.com/watch?v=-vi-5PisiDY

"Pill Bug" (video)
www.youtube.com/watch?v=DWW8Caur8Co

More Books to Read

Ansberry, K. 2020. *Nature did it first: Engineering through biomimicry.* Nevada City, CA: Dawn Publications.
Summary: This delightful introduction to biomimicry for young readers weaves together poetry and nonfiction.

Becker, H. 2014. *Zoobots: Wild robots inspired by real animals.* Toronto: Kids Can Press.
Summary: This book for older readers (grades 3–6) explores the world of robo-animals, or zoobots. Twelve double-page spreads reveal vivid, Photoshop-rendered illustrations of robot prototypes such as the bacteria-inspired Nanobot, which can move through human blood vessels, and the OLE pill bug, which can fight fires. Each spread shows a smaller illustration of the animal on which the zoobot is based.

Hughes, M. 2004. *Pill bugs.* Chicago: Raintree.
Summary: Simple text and full-color, up-close photographs in this book for young readers describe

Name: ______________________________

Pill Bug Observations

Make a sketch of your pill bug in the box below. Label any parts you know.

How many legs does your pill bug have? ______________________

Observe your pill bug's body parts. What do you notice?______________

____

____

Observe what your pill bug does when you do the following things:

What I Do	What My Pill Bug Does
Gently touch it	
Gently turn it over	
Move it to a dry place in the container	

Name: ______________________________

My Pillbot

Name of my pillbot: ______________________________

Labeled sketch of my pillbot:

1. The problem my pillbot solves: ______________________________

______________________________.

2. The part of my pillbot that is like a real pill bug:

______________________________.

3. A real pill bug uses this part to ______________________________.

4. My pillbot uses this part to ______________________________.

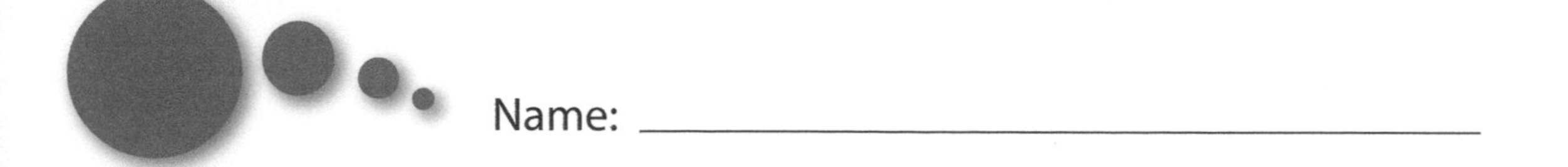

Name: ______________________________

STEM Everywhere

Dear Families,

At school we have been learning about **pill bugs**—how they move, breathe, and defend themselves. We have also been learning about **biomimicry**—how engineers try to mimic, or copy, living things to design robots and other technologies. To find out more, ask your learner the following questions and discuss their answers:

- What did you learn?
- What was your favorite part of the lesson?
- What are you still wondering?

At home, you can watch a video together about a robot called "Spot" that was inspired by dogs. Scan the QR code or go to *www.bostondynamics.com/spot* and click on the Launch Video.

After you watch the video, you can design your own robot together based on a different animal.

Sketch of Real Animal	Sketch of Robot